COVENANT

Photographs by
AL CLAYTON

Words by
WILL D. CAMPBELL

PEACHTREE PUBLISHERS

Atlanta

Published by
Peachtree Publishers, Ltd.
494 Armour Circle, NE
Atlanta, Georgia 30324

Library of Congress Cataloging in
Publication Data will be found at the end
of this book.

Peachtree books are available for bulk
purchases at special discounts for sales
promotions, premiums, fund-raising,
or educational purposes. For details,
contact our Special Sales Manager at the
address above or phone (404) 876-8761.

MANUFACTURED IN THE UNITED
STATES OF AMERICA

10 9 8 7 6 5 4 3 2 1

Design by Ken Thompson

ISBN 0-934601-83-6

for the love of a bastard child

The photographic images and fictional characters in this collection are not literally related. They are symbolic of a far-flung family depicted in fact and fiction as Southerners. Like the Biblical tribes of Israel, the people of the South have clung to a remnant of common identity throughout their history as if by some unwritten covenant they were destined to abide.

COVENANT: FACES, VOICES, PLACES is a collective work of art and language. The photographs were made in the South between 1963 and 1989. Virtually all of the southern states are represented in this collection of images. Some of the photographs were taken as a series, but for the most part, the relationship of the photographs to one another in this collection is determined by artistic considerations.

The soliloquies, all of which were written in 1989, are fictional voices. Each is an archetype, representing hundreds of Southerners and southern experiences that the author has known and learned from during his sixty-five years in the region.

Viewing the photographs together with the fictional voices has an effect like that of standing at a distance and viewing a group of trees with their reflections in a still pond. Seeing trees with their water-mirrored images creates a different, more complex scene that reveals depth and dimension. In the water reflections, the sky, clouds, and nearby plants come into view; aspects of the trees—their shape, scale— are more apparent than can be observed standing close to and viewing the trees upright. Similarly, the photographs and soliloquies in this collection combine to give a full vision. The photography captures the many faces of the South, while the soliloquies give the photography depth, revealing the stories and experiences that could have etched the faces.

While the soliloquies reflect the photography, they also reveal a life of their own. But together these two forms of expression establish a new and more powerful basis for understanding the depth of character in the people who are portrayed. That is the aim of this collection.

"I've seed de first en de last," Dilsey said. "Never you mind me."

"First en last whut?" Frony said.

"Never you mind," Dilsey said. "I seed de beginnen, en now I sees de endin."

DILSEY.
They endured.

William Faulkner
The Sound and the Fury

Covenant
_____
Faces, Voices, Places

Velma

I wonder if she knows now. Knows that I wadn't just her cook. I did cook for her all right. For going on twenty-five years I cooked for her. And before that I fed her young. From my own breast. Suckle that Jesus meant for me to use for my own babies. She told me I was doing it just to help her wean them. But I knowed she was being plumb low-down. She'd tell them babies titty was nasty. I mean when she got tired of feeding them herself. Even when they wadn't nowhere ready to be weaned. They wadn't ready for no solid food. The babies knowed it and she knowed it too. But she'd send for me and tell them babies that if they wanted to nurse it would have to be from some old black titty. Them babies didn't know the difference between a black bosom and a white bosom. They'd hang onto my nipples like leeches. And cry their little eyes out when I left.

I washed all their clothes, done their ironing. I bathed them and combed their little cotton heads, and got them ready for school. And when they was grown I helped every one of them girls get married. Curled their hair and fixed their ruffles. And it was me that told them what to do and what not to do on their wedding night. And they never forgot it. Not a one of them ever forgot it.

One of 'em moved off to California. One to Louisville. Or one of them big places up north. Other one just over in the next county. But it didn't matter where they was. Whether they close or far, they always stopped to see

me when they come home. Most of the time before they got to her house.

And that ain't the most I done for her.

I loved her.

But she almost took that away from me one time. Almost took it away. Every time I'd do something that rubbed her the wrong way, she'd rail out at me like some ol' wet settin' hen. If my Claude had'a knowed she talked to me that way, Lord, he'd of burned her house down. And never let me go back. But I kept it to myself. Always just kept it to myself.

This one morning I'd made the coffee and taken it to her bed like I always done. Then she come dragging in the kitchen in her gown tail. It after nine o'clock. Way past time for me to be gone. Hollering for her breakfast. I put it down in front of her and she took the fried egg in her hand and slammed it at me hard as she could.

Said the egg was cold. That egg wadn't cold, for I'd just took it off when she come in.

It missed me, but it landed on the stove burner I had left on in case she wanted something else. It commenced to sizzle and smoke, the yolk running all down around the red hot coil. Wadn't no way I could stop it from stinking up the whole house. She kept yelling at me, telling me to do something. All I could do was stand there till the burner cooled off so I could get it off and clean it up.

I never was no hand to talk back to her, never did sass her no matter what she said. Just kept it inside. But something or other got into me that day. I reckon the old devil hisself. I took my apron off, hung it where I always did, and told her I didn't know what to do, but if she did she could do it herself. She followed me out the door just a hollering loud as she could. Screaming, "You impudent wretch! You wait until I tell Calvin. He knows how to take care of smart-alecky niggers!"

Calvin was her youngest boy, and he always paid me off. I went straight to his house. Told him I couldn't take it no more. Told him I wouldn't be back. He almost cried while he was counting out my pay. His wife right beside him. She told me she and Calvin didn't blame me, and that they didn't know how I had put up with so much so long.

Next morning I was right back. I was already tired, 'cause I didn't sleep a wink all night. But I was back. I had talked all night to my Jesus. He told me he knew she was mean all right; knew she said hurtful things to people who was just trying to help her. But he said she was old and couldn't look

after herself and that if I would go on back
he would help me out as best he could.
Then he said something I won't never forget.
He said if we just love the folks who's easy
to love, that wadn't really no love a-tall. He
said if you love one, you have to love 'em all.

Just about the time the sun was coming
up, me laying there without a wink of sleep,
I seen him plain as day. He was settin' there
on the side of the bed, Claude still a-snoring
on the other side. My Jesus, he put his hand
on my shoulder and when I looked up at him
he give me this big wink and said, "Velma,
there's one thing I learned two thousand
years ago. Don't let mean white folks make
trash out of you." I started gettin' up, and
just as I did, he give me another wink,
shrugged his big ol' pretty shoulders, and
when I looked around he was gone.

Now here I am, standing in the rain,
back behind the crowd in this cold Bilbo
Graveyard. Bawling with the rest of them
while they lay her down. All while the
preacher was talking I kept looking around
for my Jesus to wink at me again.

But he never did.

18

20

<u>Roger</u>

21

I never had been very religious until my wife left me. She pretty much left without warning. We married young, and I was always busy, going to school, working, involved in community activities. I really thought we had a doll-house marriage. And I thought the way to keep it that way was to work hard enough to buy her anything she wanted. It started out with a little Brownie camera and wound up with a chinchilla ranch with a hundred thousand dollars worth of equipment. When I discovered that she wanted the veterinarian to go along with the ranch, that was a little too much for me. I guess there are narrow-minded people everywhere, and I must be one of them. Anyway, she left me. Just took the three kids and moved out.

I was devastated. We had everything going for us, and then, overnight, I was all alone. Except for two dogs and five hundred chinchillas. And by then there was no market for the chinchillas and the get-rich-fast promoter of chinchilla ranching had long since skipped the country.

I tried drinking my way out of it, but it didn't work. I tried chasing pretty women, and that didn't work either. So I turned to God. I prayed for two days and nights without stopping. There was a Holiness tent revival going on down the road, and I went. I had always been a member of the Methodist Church but had never been saved. That night I was saved. I knew it the

22

23

very second it happened. I started going to the little Holiness Church in town, and three months later I received the baptism of the Holy Ghost. I was happier than I had ever been in my life. I kept on working as head of a heavy equipment company. I had made a lot of money doing that, but the first year I was saved I made more money than I had the previous five. The Lord blessed me in a way I had never been blessed before. And I gave every penny I made to Him. Not ten percent. One hundred percent. Lived off some savings I had. That year, I sent over fifteen thousand dollars to the PTL Club. Nine thousand to the 700 Club. And that much again to the Jimmy Swaggart Ministries and to Oral Roberts. And they said I was the heaviest contributor to our local church. In a year and a half, a friend and I built three new churches in Honduras. I have visited all three of them.

Well, a lot of people thought that was strange behavior. They said college educated, successful businessmen just didn't do that sort of thing. I was President of the Exchange Club at the time. And the members started looking at me funny. But they just didn't understand. They didn't know what loneliness was. How it felt to stare at a darkened ceiling at three o'clock in the morning. How it was to be awakened by the sound of your own voice in the dead of night, calling out your babies' names. All that stopped when I found the Lord. So I just let them whisper. It didn't bother me at all. Not even when I was voted out of the

Exchange Club because someone said I spoke in tongues during business meetings. I did speak in unknown tongues, but not in business meetings.

Oh, there have been some disappointments along the way. And sometimes I feel like I've been let down. But God has never let me down. I wouldn't send all that money to Jim Bakker now, knowing what I do. And since Jimmy Swaggart got in all that trouble in New Orleans I don't contribute to him. It bothered me when Oral Roberts kind of inferred that God was a terrorist— saying God would kill him if folks didn't send in forty million dollars. Plus I wasn't so pleased when Pat Robertson got so mixed up in politics. I'm not sure God cares too much who the President of the United States is.

But all in all, I wouldn't change a thing. It has been a wonderful decade for me. I'm still happy. I'm still a successful businessman. And now I'm married to the sweetest, most Christ-like woman in the world.

Some folks say I took charismatic religion too far. Maybe so. But it saved my life. How can you be too extreme in the faith?

I went to every kind of religious meeting I heard of. I even went to a service up in the mountains where the worshipers were picking up serpents. I was impressed. You have to believe something a whole lot to pick up a handful of rattlesnakes. I admired them for believing that much. Me? No, I know I don't believe that strongly. Not anything. I'm scared to death of snakes. But maybe the real reason is that I'm too educated to do that.

I won't ever test my faith like that. But way down deep inside, where I really live, I wish that someday, perhaps, maybe, I just might.

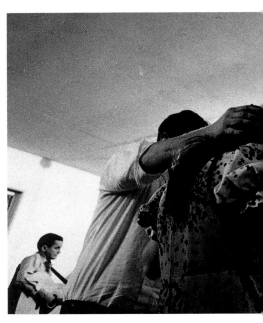

32

Doyle K. Goodall, IV

I can't figure out why my granddaddy keeps sending me these old seventy-eight rpm records. Every few weeks, I get a stack of them in the mail. Now here's a new batch. "Soldier's Joy." Some old man they called Uncle Jimmy Thompson playing a frigging fiddle on the radio. Granddaddy says in his letter his daddy saw Uncle Jimmy one time in Nashville. On the Grand Ole Opry. Brought him this very record. And Uncle Dave Macon. He played a banjo. "'Leven-Cent Cotton, Forty-Cent Meat." Wonder what that's about? Everybody had to be "Uncle." Wonder why? DeFord Bailey. "Pan-American Blues." Let's see what the old fellow says about DeFord. Says he was the only black guy to be on the Grand Ole Opry until Charley Pride came along. Now who the hell is Charley Pride? Wonder if he was ever with Black Sabbath? Hey, here's DeFord's picture. God, he looks like a little monkey playing a harmonica. Granddaddy says they called it a French harp. All right. French harp it'll be. Who cares?

I'd like to know what I'm supposed to play these things on. Seventy-eights. They won't fit my compact disc player, that's for sure. Man, these things are heavy.

Last time, he sent me some old forty-fives. Ernest Tubb, Jim Reeves, Hawkshaw Hawkins and Patsy Cline. Never heard of them either. He said they were of his generation, and he wanted me to know about them. Oh, well. Humor the old fellow. My mother says it's hard for him to understand

35

that I'm almost sixteen years old now. I played them. Once. They never would make it with my friends. Wonder what folks did for music back in those days.

I wonder if Granddaddy has ever seen Ozzy Osborne. *That's* music! Something you can hear. Yeah. Next time he comes to visit, maybe I'll get him into some metal. That'll be a trip! Maybe a pill or two. Get him in the club. Blow a joint with us. Just Say No. Ho, ho, ho. Just say no to Just Say No. What's a boy to do?

Just one little toot for Just Say No. Now where's my spoon? Dammit, where the hell's my spoon?! It was right here in this drawer. Right by the straw. Guess I'll have to snort the whole stash. Not much left anyway. Thanks to Greedy Grady Graham. After this I'm quitting. No more trips.

Here we go. This ought to get me out of the old phone booth. Soooar! It's a bird! It's a plane! It's Doyle K. Goodall the Fourth! Not First, Second, or Third. The, by-god, Fourth! Wheee! Roar, Doyle the Fourth! Roar you bastard!

———————————

"Shhhu. Hey, Gramp. Wanna see Ozzy bite a live bat's head off? Wanna see Alice Cooper kiss a cobra? I've got it on video. You say you want to talk about the old days? Wait'll Mother gets home. She likes to talk about the Monkees. Whoever they were.

"Wanna watch some TV? Violence? What kind of violence? Aw, they're not really killing and raping all those women. They're just pretending. When they turn the cameras off all the dead and raped ones get up and go home. It's just to entertain us. Teaching us? Teaching us what? Everybody already knows all that stuff. Where'd we learn it? We just know it. Everybody knows it.

"Mother doesn't get home from the office until seven o'clock. And tonight she's going out with some dude that looks like a big zit. Said she'd be late. Read a book? I have to do that in school. Come on, Gramp. Yeah, I know your great granddaddy fought with General Stonewall Jackson at Bull Run. You told me that. You told me your grandmother owned the biggest farm in Greene County, Alabama, and ran it herself. And your daddy used to put geese in the cotton fields to eat the wiregrass from around the plants, and hang gourds on pine poles to attract purple martins to eat the mosquitoes and that's why your family never had malaria. But this is Miami, Gramp. This isn't the farm. I've never even seen a cotton field and I don't know a goose from a chicken. And, wiregrass? I wouldn't know how to light it.

"I'm going out for a while. Naw. Don't bother to wait up. I have my own key."

44

<u>Bill</u>

My son wadn' hardly nothin' more than a boy when he got into the Move-ment. Nawh, wadn' hardly more than a boy. His mama didn' want him mixed up in all that mess. Me neither. But nothin' would do him but to get right there in the middle of it. 'Course, we knowed he was right, even at the time. Colored folks couldn' vote then. Couldn' go to town an' buy a hamburger 'ceptin in some colored juke joint where we didn' want him hangin' out. Couldn' go to school where the white chirren did. Couldn' ride on the bus 'lessen they set in the back. All kinds of things. It wadn' that we blame him so much. It was jes we didn' want him gittin' in no trouble. None of our folks never been in no kind of trouble. Many atime I had to bite my tongue to keep from gittin' in trouble wid the white folks. But me and my brothers, six of 'um, we never been in no trouble.

He wadn' gone six weeks 'fore we heard he was in jail up in Tennessee. Preacher here, he preached agin it. At first he did. Later on he change though. Said them younguns runnin' off, tryin' to eat in places wid the white folks, where they wadn' wanted in the first place, wadn' nothin' but triflin' niggers. He said it just like that.

We wadn' gone set there an' listen to nobody talk about our boy that way. Right or wrong, he our own flesh and blood. We didn' go back to church for the longes' time. 'Course, we shamed of it too. Him being locked up in some ol' jailhouse. Folks say

47

that be on his record from now till dooms-
day. Say he wouldn' be able to git no job,
git in the army or nothin' cause he been a
criminal. Like I say, the preacher change
later on, but that 'uz the way he talkin' at
first. His mama jes a squallin'. Hollerin',
"We lost our baby. We lost our baby." In our
family, far back as we could trace, it always
been a disgrace to git put in jail.

But the boy, he kep writin' to his mama.
Tellin' her he doin' it for our sake. For the
colored people everywhere. That what we
was called back then, wanted to be called:
Colored people.

Later on, the boy, when he come home
to visit, tole us not to say colored no more.
He said we was Ne-groes. Back when I
was comin' on, you meet up with somebody and he call you a Negro, well, lot of
folks didn' know how to say that word and it
sound too much like nigger. And no colored
person ever wan' hear that word. That 'uz
when I had to bite my tongue, when some-

body call me or one of my chirren nigger.

Wadn' long, my boy say we ain't Negroes no more. We black. Black and proud. We was proud all right, but it took some gettin' use to for me and his old mama. Back when we was comin' on, somebody call you black, almost as bad as callin' you nigger. But we done best we could to go along. Now days, the younger people tellin' us we ain't black. We African-American. I reckon we'll get use to that too. But they's only so many changes a body can take in one lifetime. When I was a lil' boy, folks plant the crop with oxen. And pick it by hand. Now they plants it from a airplane. Fertilize it that way too, and pick it with a machine half big as my house. That's a lots of changes. Lots of changes to get use to. Put that on top of not knowin' what to call yoself or what you gone be called next. From nigger to African-American. Lots of changes. Ox team to jet airplanes. Lots of changes.

Back to the boy you askin' 'bout. Next thing we knowed, he back in jail. Us thinkin' he off in college. Freedom ridin.' On a bus from Nashville to Birmenham. Back in jail. And Bull Connor done let him get beat half to death to boot. Picture in all the papers. On the TV. We seen him layin' there bleedin' in the bus station. Six white men standin' over him. Kickin' at him. Police just a-watchin.' Doin' nothin' to stop um. His mama screamin' agin. "We lost our baby! We lost our baby!" Him twenty, twenty-two years old by then. 'Course he was the baby too. Him bein' the youngest and all.

All the time though, he kept writin'.' And visitin' too when he could. Tellin' us we raised him right. Raised him to do the right thing. Next thing we knowed, he workin' right here in the county. Registerin' folks to vote. Tryin' to anyhow. Most the time jus' gettin' turnt back. Yessir, we was worried. Plumb worried sick. Scared he gone get killed. White feller from up north did get killed. Our boy been with him that same day. Later on, a white lady too.

Next thing we knowed, it was that big march. Boy say they gone march from Selma to Mister Wallace's place in Montgomery. Boy say they gone pass right by our house. White man say, he catch any of his niggers out there they might as wells to pack up. Say he wadn' gone put up with no more foolishness.

We seen 'um comin.' 'Bout half hour by sun. Our boy right up in front of the line. His mama jerk her apron off, put her Sunday

hat on and lit out, me right behind her, tryin' to pull my overhalls on. Didn' even tie my shoes. We hadn' even talked about it. Both of us so proud of that boy by then we 'bout to bust. "My baby leadin' the Move-ment! My baby leadin' the Move-ment." They wadn' no sad tears. Both of us blubberin' for joy. That boy, he stopped the whole line. A mile of folks stoppin' when our baby stopped, and him huggin' us like he wadn' never gone turn us loose. So full he couldn' even say a word. Dreckly he commence to march agin. Me and his mama right solid behind him. I reckon we musta marched till midnight. Everybody singin', "Keep on a-walkin'. Keep on a talkin'." When they bedded down for the night we turnt aroun' and head for the house. Boy walk with us for the longes' time. Then he say, "Mama, I got to leave you now. Got to git on back. It's cause I love you, Mama. It's cause I love you." 'Course, by then we already knowed that. Me and her both.

55

You know where that boy is right today? Detroit City. Yessir. That's him awright. That's the very one you got his picture there. He made a lawyer. Then made a judge. Fed'ral judge. Lots of changes I seen in my day. Lots of changes.

We don' hardly ever see the boy no more. I know he awful busy. Makin' them laws work right and all.

Sometimes, late at night, jes 'for she goes off to sleep I hear his mama sayin', "We lost our baby. We lost our baby."

In a way, I reckon we did.

60

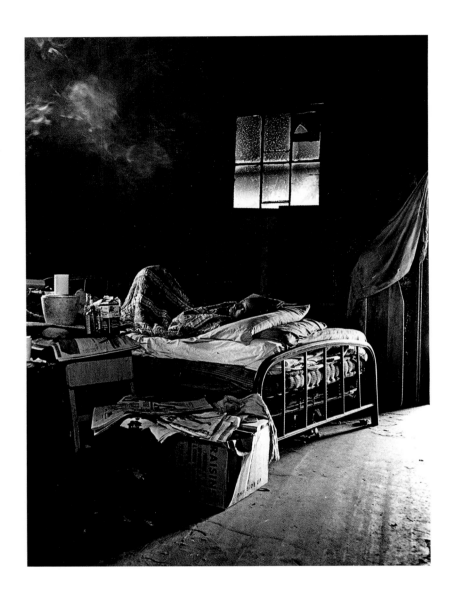

66

68

<u>Allen</u>

They said Mr. Roosevelt was going to be our salvation. In a way I suppose he was. And in another way I suppose he didn't do us any favors.

We got electric lights all right. We didn't have to bury fifty pounds of ice in a sawdust pit to make ice cream on the fourth of July or have cold chocolate milk during the summer. And make the block last until the next time the ice man came by. That was real nice. But now the electric bills are so frazzling high some months we can't afford to pay them.

About the time we got all the benefits of the REA, the war come along and most of us got good jobs in defense plants. Except the young boys who had to go off to fight. We were too busy to cut firewood for winter any more, so we got butane tanks and stopped up all the fireplaces with gas heaters. Now though, a tank of gas costs ten times what it did back then. And the chimneys are all messed up, so even if we took the heaters out we couldn't burn firewood.

They used to say Mr. Roosevelt was the one who ended the Depression. Now they're saying he's the one who got us in the war. I always was told it was because the Japanese bombed Pearl Harbor that Sunday morning. But I guess there are a lot of things that went on behind the scenes that we never knew about. I didn't have to go myself because our daddy died about the time the war started, and we had this

70

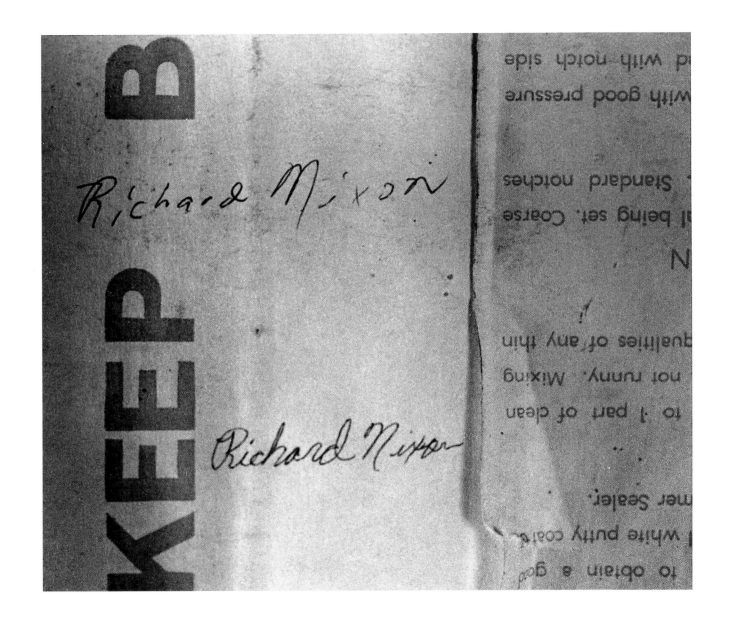

pretty good size farm, and I was declared an essential industry. All three of my brothers had to go though. I was almost too old to be drafted, but it was this farm that kept me out.

And I did the best I could with it. Of course, by the time the war actually started there wasn't a great deal to do on it. Back in the Depression, the government told us we could plant only so much cotton. I remember they sent somebody from town out here to measure our acreage, and we had to plow up more than thirty acres. Cotton that was already made. Big bolls the size of lemons, ready to pop wide open. In fact, a lot of it did open after we plowed it under—what the dirt didn't cover. But we weren't allowed to pick it. Had to just let it lie there for the winter rains to rot it.

The government had us kill a bunch of our hogs too. Just shoot them and drag them out in the woods for the buzzards to eat. That didn't make much sense, but they said it would make the price of hogs go up. Far as I can remember it never did.

Next they talked us into planting kudzu on the vacant land. And setting out black locust trees. Said they were mighty good for fence posts. I don't recall that we ever cut a single fence post out of those locust patches. Locust wasn't native to this area. Slash and loblolly pines were. If we had just left the land fallow, nature would have taken care of it. Nature is a wonderful thing. How many times have you heard me say that?

This is piney woods country. The wind would have blowed the seeds in there, and by now they would be giant sawlogs. Plus we could have cut pulpwood in eight years and telephone poles in fifteen. In twenty years we could have been thinning it out for lumber. That was fifty years ago. Law me, the rest of the trees would be so big by now two men couldn't reach around one. Timber is going for a pretty price now. Or so I've been told.

Anyway, instead of that, the kudzu has covered the ground, and the little pine seedlings can't get a start. If anybody has ever found a use for kudzu, I swear I don't know what it is. They said it would make good hay. Godamighty! Let it dry and throw it in the hay loft, and by the time you got it up there all the leaves had shed off the stems. Cows wouldn't touch it. So instead of being timber rich we're kudzu and locust poor.

But we've managed to hold onto the land. Three hundred acres of it. Twice we almost lost it to the county for taxes. Both times they had it advertised for a tax sale. Both times we barely managed to scrape together enough to pay it off. I couldn't take it if we was to lose this piece of ground. My daddy owned it and his daddy before him. Lots of folks around here lost their land to the banks or the timber companies. We've been able to hold on. At least so far. You lose your land, and you're in the road. This old house ain't much, but it's free and clear. Nothing owed on it. Even though all those programs Mr. Roosevelt come up with almost lost it for us.

On the other hand, I remember our old daddy talking about Hoover carts until the day he lay down and died. The Republicans wouldn't have done any better by us. That's for damn sure. I reckon we oughtn' to complain.

82

<u>Aaron</u>

What paper you say you're from? Don't believe they deliver that one around here. But yeah, I'll talk to you. I don't have anything to hide. Never did for that matter. For all I know you're from the police. 'Course, I don't have anything to hide from them either you understand. They've been swarming all over this whole place for two days. Looking for explosives. Looking for guns. Looking for God knows what.

Yeah, that's my boy they've got locked up. **I** don't think he had anything to do with the killing, but I reckon we don't ever know what somebody else will do. Not even our own young. I went over to the jail yesterday and tried to see him. They wouldn't even let me in. I was going to come right out and ask him if he was mixed up in it. He's my boy. And I'll stand behind him no matter what. I do know we tried to raise him right—to know right from wrong. But this day and time it's hard to figure right and wrong sometimes.

No, I don't care if you turn your tape recorder on. Like I said, I don't have anything to hide. But I'd rather you didn't talk to his mother—ask her questions and all. She's awful tore up about the whole mess. She hasn't been herself since our oldest boy was sent home from Vietnam in a box. Fighting a war he didn't know any more about than Adam's housecat. But he went. Volunteered even before they drafted him.

Said he'd have to go anyway.

He was a smart boy. Made good grades in school. Wanted to go on to college, but we couldn't afford to send him. He said maybe he could go on his GI money when he got out of service. He wanted to be an eye doctor. His grandma went full blind before she died. He always thought if she had got the right glasses soon enough it wouldn't have happened. He would have make a good one. He loved his grandma. Loved to help poor people too. He'd have made a good one. But he's gone now. And like I told his mother at the time, no amount of grieving is going to bring him back.

But it was hardest on her seeing some of the slick-talking town boys getting draft

board exemptions for such silly little reasons. Some of the boys really dumb to boot. Going to college way off somewhere just to keep from getting drafted. Running off to Canada or somewhere to get out of going to the war. Our boy wouldn't do any of that. He went in February, and in August he was back. Dead. I was in World War Two, but that one seemed a little different. We had to stop Hitler. And we did it. Besides that, my daddy was gassed in France in the first war, and never was able to work. But he got by. Never had nothing to speak of but he got by.

I'm not trying to excuse the boy that's in jail. But he never did get over his brother getting killed either. Wouldn't go to school. Hung around with what we thought was the wrong crowd. And then got mixed up

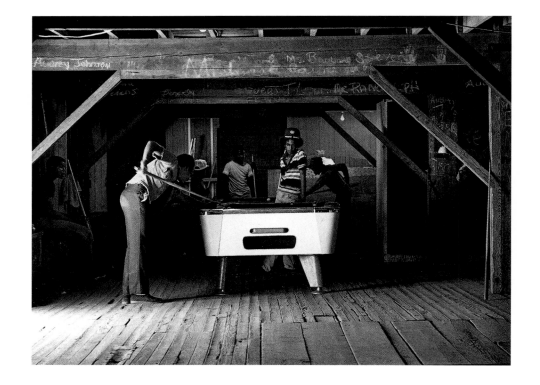

with that Ku Klux Klan outfit. I don't know for sure what they do. We never had anything against colored people. Of course, we didn't raise our boys to believe in social mixing, marrying outside their race, things like that. But that's because that's what the Bible teaches. We sure didn't teach them to hate colored people.

No, you're not taking up too much of my time. My boy's in jail and they won't even let me take him cigarettes and a toothbrush. So I reckon I've got all the time you need.

No, the boy has got a point. He said the colored folks has the N-double ACP, the Jews have the Anti-Defam…whatever-it-is League, and if the plain ordinary white folks join the Ku Klux, the law harangues them to death. He didn't like it, and I don't much blame him for it.

Of course, like I said, I'm not trying to take up for him, trying to excuse him, whether he did something wrong or whether he didn't. And I'm not saying he did or he didn't.

But I do know some things just ain't right. And my boy knew it too. Whether he had anything to do with it or not, I'm not saying. But he told me this more than once. I mean, after that bunch that called themselves the Communist Workers Party, the CWP—whatever they called themselves— come in here agitating.

I mean, listen here. You seem to be a smart young feller. And I don't care if you print what I'm saying or not. Maybe somebody will read it and can explain to me what

my boy was talking about. The preacher come out here the other day, and I asked him. He just sort of tiptoed around it. Wouldn't say one way or the other. You know how preachers are. And I asked the sheriff the same thing the day he come out here to get him.

So maybe you can tell me if this makes any sense. They take one of my boys halfway 'round the world and tell him to kill folks in some little foreign country because the government says they're Communists. And don't get me wrong. Ain't no love lost between my boys and the Communists. Me neither for that matter. We'd kill Communists for our country any day of the week. Including Sunday. Naturally, we'd rather not kill somebody on a Sunday, but we would if we had to. That's the ox in the ditch. The Bible teaches us about the ox in the ditch. But looka here. They take one boy off to kill folks

when he don't know if they're Communists or not. He gets killed. The government pays for his funeral, gives us a big American flag and shoots off guns over his coffin. Then a bunch of riff-raff come in here from up north, saying right out in public and in print that they're Communists. Bragging about it. Having rallies and carrying signs and making speeches. Putting up posters all over

the place saying DEATH TO THE KLAN—which means DEATH TO MY BOY.

I mean, if he was with the Klan, and I'm not saying one way or the other, you understand. But let's just say he was. And let's say he took his gun and went over to Greensboro and shot the folks who admitted and bragged about being Communists. Now. Here's all my boy wanted to know. And you tell me if it makes any sense for the govern-

ment that teaches us to hate Communists from the day we're born to come and lock that boy up and not even let his old daddy take him a toothbrush or a pack of Carolina-made cigarettes.

No, I don't reckon I have anything else particular that I want to say. Except that this family, poor and ignorant as we might be, loves this country. But this country ought to get its story straight. I mean, about who we're supposed to kill and who we're supposed to let live.

My boy may not be the smartest thing in the world. He might not be able to figure out hard questions like that the way his dead brother could have. But by damn, smart or not, he's a pretty fair shot. I can guarantee you that, because I'm the one that taught him how to use a gun.

But, like I say, I ain't saying he did it or he didn't do it.

92

<u>Amy</u>

93

Maybe I shouldn't have said what I did
to that writer from Philadelphia, but I did.
"And what would you do if you had a plantation?" I asked him.

I know all the facts and myths about life
on the plantation, about Simon Legree and
Little Eva. I know that in the past it was,
for the most part, an evil and cruel system
that never should have existed. But it did
exist. And still does. I didn't start it, and
I couldn't help being an only child. And a
girl, at that. When my father died, he left it
to my mother and the same overseer ran it.
When my mother died, she left it to me.
I dismissed the overseer the day after the
funeral and have been managing it myself
for thirty-four years. I think I have done
an estimable job.

It's a business. We don't have field hands,
we have employees. Some of them make
minimum wage and some of them make
twenty-five dollars an hour. We have a cotton
gin that is operated by a computer. The
man who operates it makes forty thousand
dollars a year. We grow cotton, soybeans
and peanuts. And yes, some years, we
make a lot of money; some years, we don't
make any. It depends on the weather and
the economy.

I did not dispute the man when he said
I could have divided the land and houses
equally when Mother died and given it to
the workers. Where would it be now? Where
would they be now? The truth is, I don't

95

know. I can only guess. I didn't do that then. I wouldn't do it now. Call me a Stoic. Call it paternalism, noblesse oblige, or call it greed. The land has been in my family for five generations. How the others conducted their affairs is something they are now being rewarded or punished for. Judgment Day comes to us one at a time. I don't go in for corporate guilt, the sins of the fathers and all that. I'll answer the questions put to me when the time comes. I could have sold it, as the man said, and given the money to the poor. So could have the Mellons, Fords, and Rockefellers. But they didn't, and I didn't.

I employ approximately three hundred people. Counting spouses and children, that means about fifteen hundred mouths depend on this operation. The houses aren't shanties, and they aren't mansions, but they are clean and comfortable. Yes, they all belong to me. The rent they pay is a lot less than if they were living in town and working in a factory. And no one will ever convince me they aren't better off here than they would be living in Chicago or Detroit.

He asked me how I would feel about my workers being in a union. I told him when I was twenty-five and my father was running the show, I would have been all for it. I dropped out of Bryn Mawr for two semesters and did textile organizing in North Carolina. How would I feel about a union now? Just write down, "The lady declined to answer," I replied.

Then I added, "Look, Mister. Let me sum it up for you. I'm a Democrat, a member of the DAR, the Presbyterian Church and on the Board of the Memphis Country Club. I get along with my neighbors, am generous with charities, teach literacy once a week at the state penitentiary, and work in the hospital two days a month as a nurses' aide. I don't smoke or take other hard drugs. I give my workers two weeks pay as a Christmas bonus and no one has said "nigger" on this plantation in thirty-four years. Now, if you will excuse me I have work to do," I told him.

I did not mean to be discourteous.

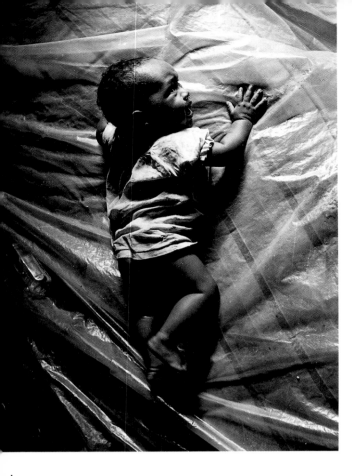

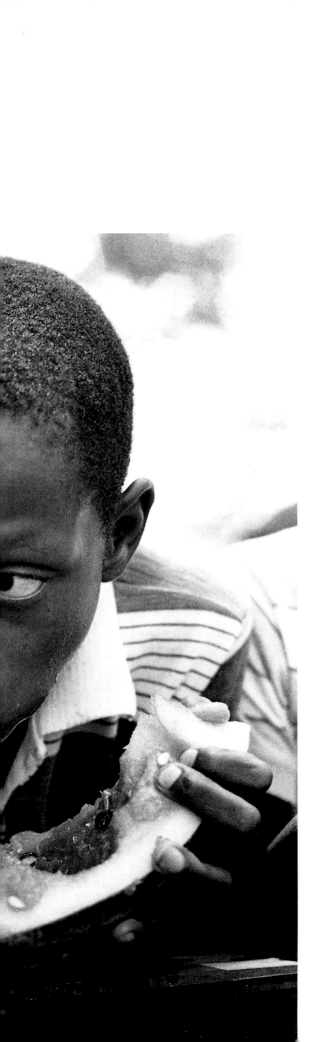

106

108

Yessir. Launey. L-a-u-n-e-y. It sounds like Lonnie when you say it but my name ain't Lonnie. It's Launey. Launey Bass.

Who'd you say sent you over here? Census? How many questions you have to ask me?

Woman come in here a few months ago. Said she was from the health department in Raleigh. Asked me fifty dozen questions. What you eat? How much hog lard? Your cows been tested for Bangs? Your dogs had mad dog shots? You ever had malarial fever? All kinds of stuff. I answered most of them best I could. Pretended I couldn't hear part of the time. Before she left she asked me if there was any special program I could think of for people like me. I told her I liked "Amos and Andy," but they took it off the air.

Just about everybody has moved out of these hollows now. The Corps took most of the good land. Making lakes. Dams. All kind of things we didn't need. One of my brothers had a big river bottom place. Government took it for a camp-a-port. You know what a camp-a-port is?

Yessir, I know you're the one supposed to be asking the questions. So ask yourself this question. You know what a camp-a-port is? I didn't. My brother didn't either.

Government said that was a recreational facility. Said it was for the folks. We didn't know what a facility was neither. After they took his land—'course they paid him what they said was fair market price, even though

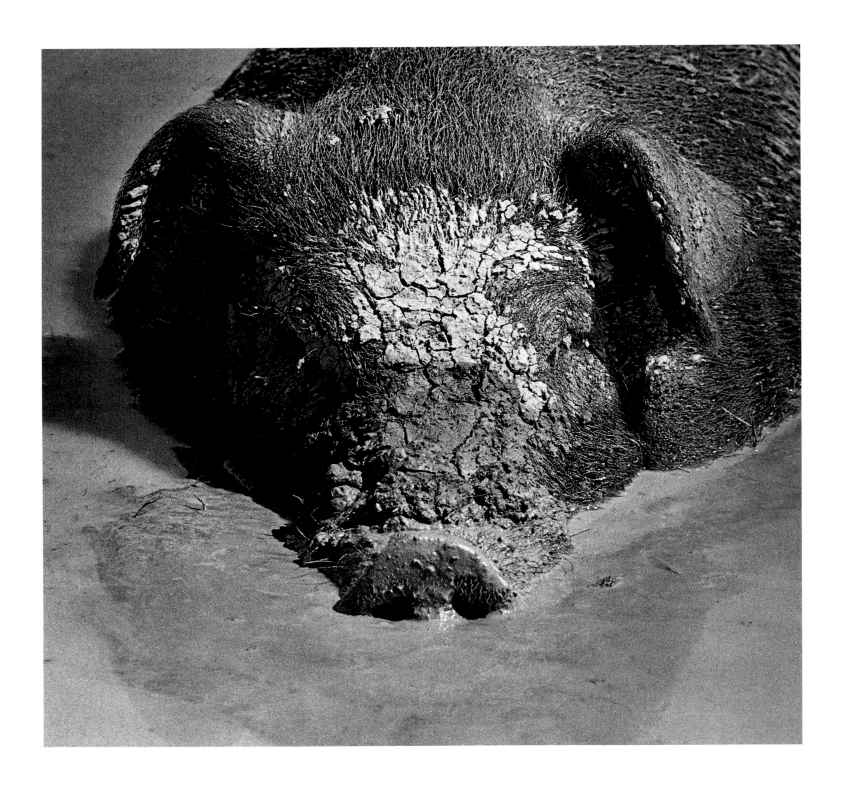

he didn't want to sell it—we found out a recreational facility is a place where jet airplanes fly in and the folks take their tents out and camp alongside the runway. I don't know no folks who's got a jet airplane. They's different folks I reckon. My brother lives in a trailer house in town now.

Yessir, I reckon we've been studied about as much as anybody in the world. Including the Indians over on the other side of the mountain. Studied. Studied. Studied. I told a feller one time they already knew more about us than they could stand. He didn't think much of that.

You say you're just taking the census? That's Washington ain't it?

Sixty-seven. I'm sixty-seven year old.

My address? If you don't know where I live, how did you get here? Yessir, I understand you're just supposed to write down what I tell you, but if you already know something, I don't see why you can't write that down without asking.

Can't you tell what race I am? There ain't nothing but white people on this whole side of the mountain, and everybody and his brother knows that.

Awright! White! My race is white.

One. Just me. My wife's dead. Been dead going on nine year.

Six. Four girls and two boys. All grown. Another one died before it was born.

I don't know what it was—boy or girl.

I don't know what its name was. It didn't have a name.

You'll have to put down that they's seven children? Mister, I don't much care what you put down. All I know is that we raised six children, and my wife had a mishap on one after she had been carrying it about six weeks. So you put down what you want to.

Forty-nine acres. That's what the deed calls for, but I really think there's more than that. Hard to tell around here. The deeds go way back. This one goes back to around eighteen hundred. Even before that.

My occupation? Can't you tell I'm a farmer? No, I ain't never been retired. Not that I know of. I worked in a cotton mill for eight years when the babies was coming along. Paper mill after that. But I was a farmer all that time. It's hard to retire from forty-nine acres of the side of a mountain.

You mean last year? Half an acre. That's all the 'backer base they'd give me. And that's dark fire. Burley don't do too well around here. I got twenty acres I could put in 'backer, but they won't let me.

'Bout eight hundred dollars I reckon.

Exactly how much? No idea. No I don't keep no records. I took cash for it. Same way with hogs and calves.

How many? Which one? Okay. Hogs first. 'Bout twenty. I think. Had three sows. No boar though. Used a neighbor's boar. How much did I pay him? Nothing. I didn't pay him nothing. Right now I got three barrows and I'll probably divide some hams and sausage with him. Maybe give him a middlin' of side meat.

A barrow? What's a barrow? You know what a gilt is. Or do you? You must not be from around here.

Whoa now! Nosir, I ain't going into that with you. I've tried to answer all your questions as best I can. I've told you my name. And I've told you my race and my address, even though you already knew all that. I've told you how much money I think I made last year and how many sows I've got. And I've told you what a barrow is and what a gilt is. But I ain't telling you where I relieve myself. Indoors or outdoors…my plumbing ain't none of your bidness. And it ain't none of Uncle Sam's bidness. I spent almost three years fighting for the right to mind my own bidness. From Bougainville to Saipan. Nobody asked me nothing about no indoor bidness then. And they ain't gonna ask me now.

Well, Mister, just bring him on. If you want to bring the sheriff out here to plunder through my house looking for where I do my bidness, bring him on. But for the sake of your census, I wouldn't advise you to come with him. Me and the high sheriff get along real well. Fact is, we haul pulpwood together in the summertime. But I reckon I shouldn'a told you that.

Yessir, I know you got the right to bring him out here. But if I know the high sheriff, he'll side with me on one thing. Where I do my bidness is my bidness.

120

<u>Miles</u>

STATE OF MISSISSIPPI   ATTALA COUNTY

I, John C. Bristow of the state and county aforesaid, being very weak of body but of perfect mind and memory, calling to mind the mortality of my body and knowing that it is appointed to all men once to die, do make and ordain this and no other my last will and testament. That is to say—principally and first of all, I commit and resign my soul to God who gave it, with the hope of its salvation through the merits of Christ my only redeemer, and my body I recommend to the earth to be buried at the discretion of my executors in a decent Christian manner, and as touching such worldly goods as it hath pleased God to help me with in this life I bequeath, divide and dispose of the same in the following manner and form.

First, all my just debts to be paid out of my estate after my decease and before any other disposition be made. After such payments I will and desire the whole of my estate to be enjoyed by my heirs or legatees as follows viz.

I will and bequeath unto my beloved son Charles Bristow ten dollars out of my estate which is to be his full share and portion of my estate.

I will and bequeath unto my beloved son Leon Bristow one hundred dollars out of my estate extra to be applied to educate said Leon in literature.

123

I will and bequeath all the balance of my estate both real and personal to be equally divided between my five sons, namely: William Bristow, John Bristow, Miles H. Bristow, Fletcher Bristow and Leon Bristow, but not Charles Bristow.

I hereby nominate, ordain and appoint as executors of this my last will and testament my beloved sons William Bristow and John Bristow, joint executors.

Signed, sealed, pronounced and declared by the aforesaid John Bristow as his last will and testament the eighth day of August in the year of our Lord One Thousand and Eight Hundred and Twenty-Six, and in the fifty-first year of the Independence of the United States of America.

SIGNED: JOHN C. BRISTOW
WITNESS: JAMES DENMAN, WILLIAM GARDNER, ELIZABETH KENNON

That was my great, great granddaddy. And he signed it a hundred and sixty-three years ago. This country was pretty new then. I believe he said it was fifty-one years old. Now it is two hundred and fourteen years old. They tell me I'm in perfect health, but I suppose I had better make out my own last will and testament before the country gets much older. I have already seen the three score years and ten the Good Book promised, plus a four year bonus. I suppose that is a pretty good indication that the sands of time are running out on me.

Let's see if I can sort all this out. Not that I can remember every bit of it. John C. Bristow, who signed that will in 1826

—whoever it was that hung onto that piece of paper all these years I'll never know— would have been my great, great granddaddy. They say he and some brothers came in here from Virginia around 1780 and homesteaded five sections of land. The brothers decided to go back to Virginia and John C. bought them out for fifty dollars and a team of oxen. So what he was dividing was thirty-two hundred acres of land. And nobody knows how many slaves. I guess that was a pretty good little spread for that day and time.

I never did find out what Charles—he would have been my great, great uncle—did to get only ten dollars of all that, beloved son though his daddy said he was. I tried to get my daddy to tell me before he died, but he said he never knew. Once when I wasn't half grown I asked my granddaddy, but he wouldn't talk about it. Near as I could figure out, it had something to do with a slave girl. Grandpa did tell me that his great uncle Charles went off to the Civil War with the Jackson Rifles, fought at Chickamauga, Franklin and Shiloh. He got a leg shot off, never made more than private even though he got a bunch of medals. Said he moved off to Texas after that and disappeared.

Leon must have been sort of special. A hundred dollars, above and beyond what the others got, just to study literature, was a lot of money. I guess he did study literature and must have done pretty well with it. I grew up hearing stories about him. He became president of a college somewhere

127

up north and when the Civil War came he was a general. Except it was on the Union side. The word was that he fought at Chickamauga and Shiloh too. When I was little, I remember wondering, sometimes late at night when I was in my bed, if maybe he was the one who shot his brother's leg off. Nobody ever told me that, though. I just imagined that maybe he was the one.

One of Leon's boys was an inventor, and they say he got rich. He invented a thing that had to do with how fast a cannon could be shot. I heard that it helped us win the First World War. Of course, I don't really know that. What I do know is that Leon gave a son his portion of the land and the son sold it to the Vardamanns, even though some of the other Bristow heirs mightily wanted to buy it.

Funny thing. All that back there is clearer to me than what happened more recently. I know they kept dividing that land, selling it off, trading it for this, that or the other thing until most of it long ago got out of the family. Some of them were bad to drink and lost it that way. The Vardamanns wound up with a lot of it, but a few years ago they sold out to a big Japanese outfit. Lord, I sometimes wonder what this country would be like today if the Japanese had won that war. I spent two years fighting them in the rotten jungles, got dengue fever and almost died—and now they own my family's land.

They never got my eighty-eight acres though. That's all that's left of thirty-two

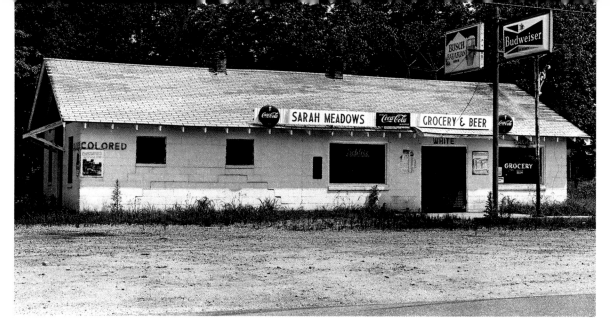

hundred. All the rest is in other hands. Now I'm about to dispose of that, too.

So who needs it? I have one boy who flies airplanes for Delta Airlines. And three girls. One of them married to the manager of a Wal-Mart store in New Orleans. One to a football coach in Oklahoma. The last one widowed at forty-two and spends her fortune going around the world. Chasing good-looking men. Nobody needs it. Nobody.

But wait a minute! She has a thirteen-year-old daughter who spends fourteen hours a day reading books. She spent last summer with me and that's all she did. I think she read every book in the county library. Two or three a day. Says she wants to go off up north somewhere and study literature.

Leona. They named her Leona. Leon. Leona. Her daddy called her "Yankee" when she was little. Blood will tell. Names too, I reckon.

Literature. Up north. H'm.

Now what the Sam Hill did I do with my fountain pen?

138

<u>Edna</u>

Sometimes it looks like things just passed us by. Going and coming.

I remember right where I was standing when Mama come and told my daddy the Depression had started. She said, "Cousin Maxine just come over and said the stock market on Wall Street crashed. Said rich folks in New York was jumping out of windows and killing theirselves. She said it looks real bad."

My daddy was fixing fence up by the Wilson place. He put his hammer down for not more than a minute. I remember exactly what he said. He said, "Well Wife, I reckon we don't have no stock on Wall Street, but we do have some stock here behind this fence. If Maxine comes back by just tell her we'll go on doing the best we can." God knows he did.

And I remember where I was standing when the mail rider come by and told my daddy the Depression was over. My daddy said he couldn't tell no difference. That was over fifty years ago and I still can't tell no difference. My life has been one long line of troubles. Work. Get sick. Go on welfare. Get blamed for that by folks who ought to know better. Never been more than twenty miles from where I was born. Not many pleasures. Snuff and a little coffee and that's about it. One new dress every few years. And that when somebody dies.

I must have done something wrong sometime in my life. At least, that's what the

preacher says when I complain. Which ain't very often. I don't do much complaining because it don't do no good to complain.

Whatever it was I done, I've paid for it a thousand times. But I know I ain't no mean somebody. I read my Bible every day of the world I'm able to. And I raised them five children pretty much by my own self. Now they're all grown and off on their own. Not but one of them any better off than I am, and that one's wife won't let him have nothing to do with any of the rest of us. I reckon she's ashamed of us because they can afford to drive a fine car and wear clothes that don't come from Sears.

The littlest of the young'uns wasn't hardly much more than a baby when their daddy took to drinking and finally run off with that bowlegged Marselius hussy.

Lord, I wonder whatever become of them. Somebody told me the county health department put him in kill-or-cure twice. I never could understand how a fellow could be killed or cured twice. Looks like it would have been one way or the other the first time. But then, he wasn't no plain ordinary sort of a drunk. Lordy mercy, I ought to know that for sure. Fact is, he wasn't no plain ordinary sort of a fellow. As long as we lived together as man and wife, I ought to know that too. And I do.

Truth of the matter is, he never was really mean to me. Nor the children neither, for that matter. And like I always told my mama before she died, I reckon if he was to walk through that door right now I'd take him back. If it had of just been the woman, I'd have won. But I couldn't fight her and the whiskey both. So I let him go.

145

147

Rhodes

Rhodes McGowen

The preacher came in here right after my old buddy left. Asked me if I was ready to go. I said, "I am now." He said he had heard that it could be any day now.

There were so many things I wanted to say to my old buddy. But this haze I'm in, bedimmed from the ailment and all the years I've been around...I just sort of wander in and out of things. I did tell him I love him, though. I remember telling him that. Something I never could have told him years back. Even though I should have. Funny how menfolks have trouble telling each other things like that. Leastwise until the pale horseman starts to gallop by the door.

WHERE AM I? AND WHO ARE YOU? YOU'RE NOT MY WIFE. SHE'S BEEN DEAD FOR TWENTY-ONE YEARS. LEFT ME IN THE SUMMER OF SIXTY—EIGHT. TWO DAYS AFTER HER BIRTHDAY. YOU'RE NOT MY DAUGHTER, EITHER. SHE HASN'T BEEN HOME SINCE HER MAMA WENT AWAY. YOU'RE A NURSE? AND THIS IS A HOSPITAL? SURE, I KNOW I'M SICK.

Must be bad sick, from what I hear them saying. 'Course they generally try to sneak around and say things. Not my buddy, though. He came right out with the truth. But then he always did. He told me I was pretty much on my way. And that it was all right. Everything was all right.

YOU SAY YOU'RE SUPPOSED TO GIVE ME A SHOT? YOU KNOW WHAT? MY BUDDY ALREADY BROUGHT ME A SHOT. MORE THAN ONE SHOT. AND I FEEL REAL GOOD.

Strange thing about me and my old buddy. I haven't seen him but a few times in sixty years. Me and him was real close when we was little. We had a secret pact back then. That we would be friends forever. I wasn't more than ten years old. We scratched each other's initials on our arms with the tips of our pocket knives. Me using his knife, him using mine. Just real shallow but deep enough to draw blood. Deep enough to make a scab and leave a scar when the scab pealed off. Guess the undertaker will see it when he lays me out. And we had a secret handshake. He was a little older than I was, and he taught it to me. Nobody ever knew it but us. Even when we hadn't seen each other for twenty years or more, we would give that secret handshake.

154

NURSE!

He came to see me after Laura Lea died. Stayed with me for a week or two. Then, when he figured I could make it on my own, he was gone. I didn't see him again until he heard I was bad sick.

We sat up most all night talking. He asked me if I had any regrets. I told him I reckoned I ought to have a lot of regrets, many crazy things as I've done in my life. But I told him I didn't really have but one. I come from a long line of bootleggers and moonshiners, and I've never made a drop of whiskey in all my born days. I told him if life lasted I was going to remedy that. Told him I was the only generation of males in the whole McGowen clan, going all the way

back to before the Civil War, that hadn't made any whiskey, and that I didn't want to be the one to break the line.

IS THAT YOU, NURSE?

I suppose he knew I was too far gone. He told me he would carry on the line for me. That we were like brothers and that he could carry on the line for our generation.

Well, now we're talking about a fellow who has lived a near perfect life. I sure as hell can't claim that for myself. My buddy, he always did the right thing. He never drank, smoked, gambled, cussed. None of that. Never chased women. Nothing. Me, I did all those things. Lots of all those things. I even did a little fighting and stealing. Got a 'leven-twenty-nine once for stealing a neighbor's bass boat. I guess I never amounted to much of anything. But my old buddy did. He worked hard. Owned a dry goods store. He didn't get rich, but he made a good living. Raised a big family of girls and every one of them amounted to something. One a doctor. Another one teaches in college somewhere. All of them doing well. He got all kind of civic awards. He never in his life even got a parking ticket. Was a deacon in his church. Taught the junior boys' Sunday School class. Helped poor children go to school. Headed up the Red Cross drive. Bought food for people when they were hard up.

I really didn't know what he was talking about when he told me he was going to carry on the line.

Now I lay me down to sleep. I pray thee Lord, my soul to . . . No that's not right. I'm not going to sleep. Excuse me, God. I wonder why it's so dark in here.

My buddy had to learn how to make whiskey from scratch. He didn't know worm from mash. And he had to dodge the law all that time. Nothing the law likes better than to bust a moonshiner. And if he's a good solid Baptist deacon, so much the better.

My buddy went all the way to Nashville. Two hundred miles. He read every book he could find on making whiskey. But there's a lot of things you can't learn reading books. The books didn't tell him much. So he went on up into Kentucky. Way up on the Kentucky River cliffs. Told his wife he was up there on business. Said he hadn't ever told his wife one lie the whole time they had been married. That was just the beginning of his sinning. He was up there more than a week before he could find somebody who would trust him. Everybody thought he was with the law. He made up one lie after another. Told some folks he was writing a book. Told some others he was with a moving picture company. Anything to try to get somebody to talk.

Finally he found this real old man, drunk at the time, who lived in a shack and didn't have a sound tooth in his head. Just rotten snags. And couldn't half see because he didn't have any eyeglasses. My buddy decided just to tell the old man the truth. Told him the whole story about me being sick, about my regret and all, and how he had promised he would carry on the line. He told the old man that if he would teach him how to make whiskey, he would pay to have all his teeth fixed and would buy him some good eyeglasses through a doctor.

That old drunk told my buddy everything. How to make a still. Beginning to end. And when he finished, he wouldn't take a red cent. He drew him pictures. Made diagrams and wrote stuff down as best he could. Started by warning him not to use anything but copper. Then he walked him through step by step, beginning with the cooker, the big pot you put the beer in after the mash has worked. Then the thumper. That's the pot that catches the settlings while the steam is forming. If you get the cooker too hot the beer will belch over into the thumper and you have to drain it out through the puker. That's the faucet at the bottom. I reckon that sounds bad, me lying here in this bed, but that's what it's called. I remember my daddy and granddaddy talking about how important that was.

Then the old man told him how to make the worm. That's the coil that goes from the thumper into the flake. That's the last big pot, and it has cold water running through

it all the time, and that condenses that hot steam back to liquid. The old man told my buddy to take a long copper pipe and wrap it round and round a tree into a coil. Then that had to be soldered onto the thumper and all that had to be done with silver solder. No lead. Ever. That's what kills people. My buddy was just going to make a tiny still, so he could make the coil by wrapping it around a chair leg or something like that. I reckon that's kinda funny. In my case.

Once he showed him how to make the still, he started in to teach him how to run it. Said you take some variety of open-pollinated white corn and have it crushed. Not like corn meal. More like chicken feed. Put just enough water over it to cover it. Then you go away for about a week. Depending on the temperature. Let the corn sour. Rot really. After that you go back and add the sugar. Equal amount. My buddy said he used fifteen pounds of corn, so he had to use fifteen pounds of sugar. Stir it real good, and fill the container up with water. He got the water right where the Tombigbee River crosses the Sumner County line. That's where me and him used to run trot lines and catch blue cats and eels when we were boys. We'd swim in there, too. Pure cold water. Then you go off and leave it again. For about another week. Let it ferment.

NURSE!!

A thick cake will form on top, and when that cake breaks up and starts to sink to the bottom, the beer is ready. Beer is what

you call the liquid from the mash after it gets through fermenting. My granddaddy used to say some of the old-timers would drink some of that, but it was real weak.

You pour that in the cooker and build the fire. Everything has to be shut down tight. He just had a little bitty still so he used butane. If it gets too hot, the old man told him, the thumper would start to shake and carry on. Thump, thump, thump. You could blow the thing sky high. You can feel the steam rising across the pipes, coming gradually over to the flake, down and around the coil going through the cold water.

God, I wish I could have been there with him when that worm broke. That's what you call it when the whiskey actually starts running out the end of the coil. At first, he said, it ran real slow. Just kind of dripping. Like an old man peeing. The old-timers, my granddaddy said, would whoop and holler and slap one another on the back and throw their hats in the air when the worm broke and they got their first taste of the new whiskey. My buddy couldn't do any of that. It was all strictly business with him. But he did tell me he was some kind of excited when the worm broke and he knew that he had actually done what he promised me he was going to do.

NURSE! IT SEEMS LIKE IT'S GETTING DAYLIGHT IN HERE. DID YOU TURN SOME BIG LIGHTS ON ME? I DON'T FEEL COLD LIKE I DID.

My buddy had him some stories to tell me about all that. And some of it give him an awful burden. He had to lie to his wife

about what he was doing. He had to do all the work on Sunday because the store was closed on Sunday. He hadn't ever worked on Sunday before. And then his wife had to lie to the people at church about why he wasn't there teaching Sunday School class, taking up the collection at the service and all. Seemed like the part about his wife having to lie bothered him the most of all. Plus having to dodge the law. Something he had never done before either. But people were talking, and he knew he had to do it. He was doing it all in a little fishing cabin he had where nobody ever went but him. Two or three times, he would meet the law on the road after he got out of the woods. But he never got scared, he said.

Never wavered and never turned back.

When the worm broke he let it fill up one little half-pint mason jar. The rest of the whiskey—and that first run must have been about a hundred and sixty proof—just ran out in the cabin.

He had rigged up twelve sticks of dynamite. One for each apostle. He said he left Judas in on purpose. He had a fuse eight yards long. Told me there were Ten Commandments, but he had broke two of them real bad. The ones about lying and working on the Sabbath. So he only had eight yards of fuse. He put the jar in his car, started the engine, lit the fuse and high-tailed it out of there. Headed for me. He said he heard it go off before he got out of sight. He knew there wasn't a splinter left or a piece of copper big enough to tell what it was. When he got to the main road, he looked back and saw a big pillar of fire and a tower of smoke. Like in the Bible. All that raw whiskey, I reckon. He said the Lord was leading him.

My old buddy sat right there beside my bed. Telling me the whole story, us passing the jar from one to the other. He said that was the first drink of liquor he had ever tasted. It for certain wasn't the first drink I had had, but I'm here to tell you it was the best. My buddy sure did learn how to make good whiskey.

When he left, he was weaving a little. I could see him through the door. There was two men standing there waiting for him. I heard one of them say, "Come on. We've been watching you. Now we got you."

I heard my buddy say, "Let's go. I'm ready now."

NURSE!!!

Colophon

COVENANT: FACES, VOICES, PLACES is a cooperative work of art involving many creative hands. Al Clayton's photographs were made in the South between 1963 and 1989. Each original photograph used for reproduction here was printed by him. The fictional people in Will D. Campbell's stories, all of which he wrote in 1989, are representative of hundreds of Southerners he has known and listened to in his sixty-five years in the region. John Egerton of Nashville provided valuable comments and advice to the author, photographer, and the publisher. Melissa Boyer of Atlanta copy-edited the manuscript. The work was united in a graphic design originated by Ken Thompson of Atlanta, who also designed the dust jacket. Mechanicals were prepared by Jacelen Pete and production was overseen by Candace Magee, both of Atlanta. The photographs were prepared for duotone reproduction by Georgia Litho of Atlanta. Type was composed at Typesters, Inc. in Atlanta on an Alphatype Multiset III in twelve point Fenice Light with eight points of spacing between the lines. Futura Extra Bold was selected as the display type. Stitched typography was created by Marcia Heirman, Atlanta. The book was printed on 80-pound Celesta Litho Dull and bound in Smythe Sewn signatures by Arcata Graphics of Kingsport, Tennessee.

Library of Congress Cataloging-in-Publication Data

Campbell, Will D.
   Covenant : faces, voices, places / photographs by Al Clayton ;
words by Will D. Campbell.
    p. cm.
  ISBN 0-934601-83-6
  1. Southern States—Social life and customs—1865- 2. Southern
States—Biography. 3. Southern States—Description and
travel—1981-—Views. I. Clayton, Al, 1934—. II. Title.
F216.2.C36 1989
975—dc20
                                                       89-16067
                                                       CIP